MW00613868

SARCOIDOSIS

(SAR – COI – DOSIS)

WHAT YOU DON'T KNOW COULD KILL YOU!

Dorothy Beatrice Goines

Printed in the United States of America

First Printing 2019

Copyright © 2019 by Dorothy Beatrice Goines

All rights reserved.

No part of this book may be used or reproduced in any manner whatsoever without written permission from the author. This includes any mechanical, photographic, or electronic process. Nor in the form of a photographic recording, or stored in a retrieval system, transmitted or otherwise copied for public or private use – other than "fair use" as brief quotations embodied in articles and reviews – without prior written permission from the author.

For permission requests, speaking inquiries and bulk order options, email **goinesdorothy@gmail.com**

Library of Congress Cataloging-in-Publication Data

Identifier: ISBN-13: 978-0-578-46924-9

Name: Dorothy Beatrice Goines

Title: SARCOIDOSIS (SAR-COID-OSIS)

Subtitle: WHAT YOU DON'T KNOW COULD KILL YOU!

Subject: Sarcoidosis

TABLE OF CONTENTS

DISCLAIMER

I am not a doctor and do not claim to offer any professional medical treatment plans or diagnoses. The reader should always consult a physician for matters relating to his/her health, particularly with respect to any symptoms that may require diagnostic or medical attention.

Some names and identifying details have been changed to protect the privacy of individuals who were willing to share details of their personal experiences. Any resulting resemblance to persons living or dead is entirely coincidental and unintentional.

I have recreated my own personal walk with Sarcoidosis by sharing some of my challenges, discoveries, questions, memories, notes, conversations and input from some of my caregivers.

DEDICATIONS

God has certainly found favor in me. I continually thank Him for my awesome support base. My family and friends continue to be the wind beneath my wings. They truly help to make it easy for me to accept the things I cannot change.

This book is dedicated first and foremost to my late parents (R.E. Goines, Sr. and LeeAnnie Goines). I am everything I am because of how they loved me and my siblings. The legacy they handed down to us by example will live forever. Because they walked the walk before us and touched so many lives and we continue building their legacy with every life we touch.

My two sons, Richard and Darin Goines, fueled my insatiable desire to live. I have an overwhelming unconditional love for them and continually appreciate the support they give me. I also cherish my eleven (11) grandchildren: Terryn, Richard, Jr., Anniah, Joseph, Darin, Jr., Samiah, James, Isaac, Faith, Sayenna and Kendrick who keep me in prayer asking God for more grace and mercy that I might be blessed to live long enough to witness some of their contributions to our legacy.

This book is also dedicated to my siblings: Rev. Henry L. Goines (deceased), Judy Davis (deceased), Roosevelt Clemons (deceased), R.E. Goines, Jr. (deceased), Dr. Beulah Lateef, Dr. Sennie Smith, Richard Goines (T-Bone), Joseph Goines, Sr. (deceased) and Dr. Jeanette Goines-Osler. In each of their own individual ways, they carried me. Regardless of my level of need, one or more of my siblings always stepped up to the plate. The unconditional love and bond between the Goines children is a priceless piece of our legacy. They each continue to nurture, support and encourage me. They have also been relentless in their insistence that I "Get The Book Done!"

Another honorable mention is Susan Taylor, my Angel of Mercy, dearest friend, ardent cheerleader, and a major source of inspiration and motivation for me. I would really be hard pressed to figure out how long Susan has been a part of our family. It seems like my entire life. She has really been another set of footprints for me. Just a look over my shoulder and she's there. She is one of my dream weavers. As a great listener who fuels my optimism and encourages me to always dream big dreams, Susan shares the belief that I can make all of my dreams come true. Her influence and support has certainly played a significant role in shaping and molding me to be the confident shaker and mover that I am.

Elliot Sterling, literally my breath of fresh air and brother by another mother, has always been only a telephone call away, ready to share his infinite knowledge of herbs and natural healing with our family. It is with great love, admiration and certainty that I attribute the extended lives of several family members (me included) to Elliot's wise and loving contribution.

Virginia Welker has been my Ride or Die Road Dog. There were very few days when Virginia and I were not talking on the telephone or riding out together. She was my "instead" person when I was too sick to take care of anything that required my attention (including my own needs). Jennie always stepped up to the plate. She often came by my apartment to get marching orders and went out to take care of my business without complaint. Virginia is so intertwined with my family, my grandchildren call her "Aunt Jennie". She is truly a Sister by Another Mother.

Rita Scott was my Champion of Faith who was always that hand I could reach out and touch. She and all the memories we made together will always have a special place in my heart.

ABOUT THE AUTHOR

Dorothy Beatrice Goines, was born and raised in Champaign, Illinois, one of nine other siblings (5 brothers and 4 sisters). As a single parent, tapping in on an extremely solid support base, she raised two sons (Richard and Darin) who blessed her with eleven (11) grandchildren. She follows in her parents footsteps by maintaining a lifelong commitment to supporting senior citizen concerns, civic causes, children and families.

She graduated from Champaign Central High School and immediately attended Southern Illinois University. She returned home two years later and attended the University of Illinois. After that, she transferred to Eastern Illinois University where she earned a Bachelor's of Science and a Master's degree in Guidance and Counseling. Prior to becoming crippled by an undiagnosed medical condition that forced her to end employment, she enjoyed a lengthy career in social work with the Illinois Department of Children and Family Services.

Prior to her disabling illness and challenges with Sarcoidosis, Dorothy was a member of the Classic Traveling All Star bowling team, competing in local, state and national tournaments. She is also one of the loudest people in the room during basketball playoffs.

She now enjoys good healthy debates and level 5 information-sharing conversations. She loves playing bingo, board games and cards. In addition, Dorothy likes movies, on stage performances, music, family gatherings and traveling.

FORWARD

God has made His presence so real in my life, by giving me the ability to put pen to paper and actually re-live so many of my experiences. When I look back over my life at where I was and where I am now, the tears of joy flow. I am humbled by God's confirmation to me that I am in His favor. He has kept me through it all because there is a great work for me to do. To paraphrase Pastor T.D. Jakes, who happens to be one of my favorite spiritual leaders. "When God has a calling on your life, he will not take it back. Even if you are not in alignment with His will and have taken a detour, your destination remains the same. God will not take it back."

In this book I have taken the bold, difficult step of opening up and sharing a portion of my personal experience with Sarcoidosis in the sincere hope that it can make a difference in the lives of others who may be experiencing some of the many symptoms I have known. Lives will be saved by reading something between the pages of this book.

The original direction of this book included a lot of scientific data and research. Later, I made the conscious decision to make the book more personal. Research findings are constantly changing; and the most current research findings are always available on Google. Furthermore, the Sarcoidosis experience is never the same for any two people on any given day. By changing the direction of this book and sharing my own personal journey, it created a comfort zone I can live with. All the trials and testimonies are personal to me.

This book will in no way answer all the questions one might have. That is not possible. There is not yet a cure for this incredibly disabling disease and research is ongoing. A lot more doors need to be opened to the address the many mysteries and questions Sarcoidosis Warriors live with every day. What is known, however, is that each individual diagnosed with Sarcoidosis will have their own unique experiences throughout their journey.

So many warriors have already lost the battle, not even knowing they were in it. It is my hope that this book will provide enough of an understanding of Sarcoidosis to inspire the reader to insist on more tests and straight answers when bringing any concerns to their doctor's attention. I want very much to emphasize the fact that because so many of the symptoms from Sarcoidosis overlap with more common diseases, it is a difficult ailment to diagnose. With this in mind, it would not be unreasonable to ask that further testing be done. It certainly benefitted me.

WHY I WROTE THE BOOK

My primary motivation for writing this book is to reach as many people as possible, sharing the knowledge I have gathered over the past 15 years about Sarcoidosis. Impressing upon them the importance of making good notes of any noticeable changes in their body that might need attention. For those who do not have Sarcoidosis (or might not know they have it), this book can serve as a wakeup call prompting them to pay very close attention to their bodies and quickly act upon any notable changes. Not doing so, could very well cost them their life.

The second motivator for writing this book is highlighted in the subtitle. "What You Don't Know Could Kill

You". This is very important because as was the case for me, many of you are going about your 'never you mind' every day and could be experiencing some of the same conditions and notable changes in your body as I was. Like me, you may well be minimizing the subtle signs your body is trying to communicate to you and not seeking medical attention or asking questions. In any case, should you be suffering with the onset of Sarcoidosis and not get a treatment plan in place, it could very well kill you. This disease has been and still is claiming lives every day. The number of deaths which could be linked to Sarcoidosis is no doubt much higher than we will ever know.

After reading this book, many of my family and friends will probably say, "Dorothy, I had no idea you were so sick and what you were dealing with. I can remember when you lost all that weight." I cannot even count the number of times people have asked me "What is that?" Each time, the desire to share my Sarcoidosis journey with others tugged at my heart. At the same time, some people who do know and love me continue to say "Girl, write the book. You will enlighten people and save so many lives."

SOMETHING WAS VERY WRONG

I believe Sarcoidosis began to manifest in my body in the year 1999. After completing a regularly scheduled annual eye examination, the optometrist noted my prescription had drastically changed since my last visit. She said should she give the full prescription, I would not be able to comfortably benefit from wearing my new glasses. It was also within this timeframe that my eyes rejected the contact lenses I normally wore every day. I have not been able to wear hard or soft lenses since 1999. Subsequently, I accepted the recommended weaker prescription and went on about my 'never you mind'.

I continued to raise my two sons as a single parent, work fulltime as a social worker and part-time as a data entry clerk. I also served on the Board of Directors for the YWCA and worked on several planning and program committees in the community. In addition, I traveled with my church and around the country bowling competitively.

Not realizing I was at the beginning of a very long journey with this disabling disease,

I continued to work at the Department of Children and Family Services until it became too much of a struggle to make it through a work day. Throughout every day, I was completely exhausted. Having insomnia robbed me of being able to get a good night's sleep. My cough had become so chronic, I was no longer able to represent my clients in court. I could not even finish a complete sentence without being bent over with a dry painful cough.

The excessive weight loss began to take a toll on me. I had gone from 277 pounds to 112 pounds in just a few months. My strength was totally drained. I had gotten to the point that the labored breathing made it extremely difficult for me to walk from Point A to Point B. Subsequently, I left my dream job, taking a non-occupational extended medical leave.

It was at this point I had to accept the reality of how terribly disabled I had become. I spiraled down into a deep depression. I was forced to realize how much of my life was compromised and how bleak my future looked, as a result of whatever was happening to me. I couldn't work, take care of my father or sons and any of my extracurricular activities were out of the question.

I have always taken pride in the fact that I was usually the one to step up to the plate as a caregiver for others. The thought of needing someone to take care of me really messed with my head. So, when family, friends and inquiring minds came by the house to check on me, I generally mustered up enough strength to get to the door to say "I'm okay, I'll be fine, Thanks for stopping by. No, I don't need anything".

As my condition continued to deteriorate, I was spending the majority of my days and nights lying in bed waiting for the Death Angel. What was consistent and persistent the whole time was my big sister, Judy. She made regular visits in and out of the house with her key. Although I never complained to her, she repeatedly advised me to go see a doctor. I said okay just to shut her up, but didn't go. Then, during one of her pop in visits and lectures I asked her to promise me she would take care of my youngest son, Darin, and make sure he finished school. It was at this point she pulled out her "I'm Not Tryin' To Hear That" Big Sister Card and insisted I get up and go see a doctor "today!"

My going to Dr. Colby was a 'no brainer' because he had been my doctor since middle school. Over the years, we had developed both a professional and personal relationship. He was my friend. The day I walked into the doctor's office I had not seen him for many years. I was unrecognizable. I had lost over 150 pounds and was pretty much skin and bones. Because of my chronic cough, I was not able to make sense when I tried to talk. I was too weak to even explain what my concerns were. I was soaking wet with sweat, but shivering cold, eyes sunken and blood shot red, barely had any hair and was completely exhausted from not being able to sleep for days, weeks, months, I didn't even know. The long and short of it: I was a Hot Mess!

When the nurse told Dr. Colby I was in the waiting room to see him but had no appointment, he came out to give me his 'Hello, How are You' hug that was customary whenever I just stopped by his office. After seeing me, he told his nurse to take me next. Prior to Sarcoidosis, I did not really have any major medical issues, so my visit was generally a stay well checkup and a visit between old friends.

I was blessed to meet Dr. Colby back in the 60's. He always completed my school physicals and addressed any other medical problems that arose throughout college and later work years. Several years often passed between our visits. I did, however, make a point of stopping by his office to say hello and get a hug whenever I was in town. He always wanted a progress report about school, the kids and the rest of the family. He never failed to remind me that I was not "just a patient" but I was also his "friend". He always insisted I keep in touch. Those times were always very positive and uplifting because he was so nurturing and encouraging. His genuine interest and concern for me was Real Love.

We shared a mutual respect for each other and a bond that surpassed any health concerns I had and any other physicians I saw throughout the years. He was always just a telephone call away to clear up any questions or concerns I might have had. He made it clear to me he wanted to stay abreast of any medical attention I needed, regardless of who the attending physician was. He willingly stood in the gap for me anytime I needed him. I trusted him totally and felt comfortable and secure with any feedback or recommendations he gave me. I knew he always had my best interest at heart. I firmly believed he would be completely honest with me whether the news was good or bad.

After my examination and follow up conversation in his office, he told me I needed to have someone come drive me to the hospital. In spite of my frailty and weakness, I tearfully told him I could not leave my Father and son. They needed me. Dr. Colby made it clear, in no uncertain terms (friend to friend), that should I not follow his directions and make arrangements to go from his office directly to the hospital, he would have to have his nurse call to make arrangements for me to go to the morgue.

ME IN THE HOSPITAL – LET THE SEARCH FOR ANSWERS BEGIN

I had been instructed by Dr. Colby to go pass the Emergency Room, "do not stop to register, they will be waiting for me in the Intensive Care Unit" where I remained for several days fighting for my life. The challenge then being to keep my lungs open, thus allowing me to breath on my own. Since that stint in the hospital, my breathing capacity has never gotten back up to 100 percent without the assistance of oxygen.

After having faxed his orders for me to the hospital, Dr. Colby came to visit that evening. He looked at test results and informed me that my diagnosis was "double pneumonia" accompanied by extreme dehydration. The treatment he started was very aggressive, including steroids and continuous oxygen. During this time, he ordered more blood and lab work.

While I am known by all of my doctors and others to make a habit of asking lots of questions, I was blessed with a friend and primary care physician who was equally inquisitive and aggressive. He pursued my health concerns with a vengeance and went above and beyond what one could even imagine. His goal was to insure I would be able to enjoy a quality of life that he could be proud to have been a part of making happen.

Dr. Colby was so committed to getting a handle on the cause of this disabling condition, he came to the hospital two times a day to look at more test results, all of which were "negative". He continued to assure me he was determined not to let me "go out like this". Stating "I am going to find the Dorothy I knew as a little girl." He went on to say "together you and I will get a handle on this." As a result, many tests were conducted, (some repeatedly) including tuberculosis, lymphoma, lupus, AIDS and cancer all of which continued to come back "negative".

After stabilizing me from my bout with the double pneumonia and the test results not giving him any sense of direction, Dr. Colby gave in to my whining and crying to be discharged and let me go home with my father and son.

I was 'over the top' happy to be back home in my own bed; away from the needles, tubes and disrupted sleep. My thinking at that time was, with all my test results being negative and no one able to figure out what was happening in my body, death was imminent. That being the case, I wanted to be at home with my family when I took my last breath.

While at home, my condition began to become more and more challenging every day to the point of me being pretty much bedridden, requiring total care. As a result of my getting weaker and weaker, I was not able to stand up on my own. My 80-year-old father, with his own set of health challenges, insisted on taking the lead in getting me back and forth to the bathroom and back in bed. That was the extent of my existence at this point. There were even some days when I could not swallow at all and my father would blend my food and spoon feed me, letting it just run down my throat. Many times, it would come right back up. He would clean me up, change my bed and put me back down to sleep. On some rare occasions, he would allow my son to help with my care.

On what I would consider a good day, I was able to chew small portions of food and get the flavor out. My father would then take it back out of my mouth and put it in the garbage. At times he would have to retrieve some of the food particles that stuck along the walls of my cheeks using Q-tips and even his fingers. My deteriorating health and level of need became much more than my father could really handle and I ended up back in Intensive Care where I was diagnosed with double pneumonia again.

Needless to say, having to go back to the hospital was very devastating for me. I felt so helpless and defeated. I just laid in that hospital bed most days in tears. Depression really had a stronghold on me and I was too weak to fight back. In my mind, I believed by the continuous flow of visitors I had coming and going they were all there to say "goodbye." Many of them didn't even speak, they just sat by my bed in silence and prayed.

I was totally convinced that the Death Angel would be coming any day, after I looked up and saw my brother, Rick (T-Bone). He had driven all the way from Houston, Texas to see me. He tells me that when he arrived at the hospital he went directly to my room but did not see me in the bed. (I was too thin, to even make a bump in the covers). He then inquired at the nurse's station about my whereabouts, nervously thinking I might have already died and been transferred to the morgue. The nurse assured him I was in my room and walked back with him to announce I had a visitor. I was not able to lift my head or turn over, so Rick came around to the other side of the bed where I was able to see his face. He tells me that when he saw my face and the big smile I had, after seeing him by my bedside, he drove back to Texas with the confidence and assurance he would see me again under more positive circumstances. T-Bone and I have had many separation challenges in our life and I am so thankful to God for allowing both of us to live long enough to let the good times we've had together out distance the bad separations.

While Dr. Colby tried to cheer me up with his not very funny jokes and constant reassurances saying "hang in there, Dorothy, we're going to beat this thing", I knew he was as frustrated and afraid as I was, but he never gave up hope. He continued to order more tests and lab work. He was relentless in his search to find some notable change that he could pursue. He always encouraged me, saying "Dorothy, I have known you too long to watch you go out like this. I will continue to run as many tests as I have to, in order to get some answers."

FINALLY A LEAD TO FOLLOW

While reviewing several sets of previous x-rays and comparing them to what was my most recent, Dr. Colby discovered a difference. Some of my lymph nodes had swollen to be the size of a golf ball. This was a marked change that was cause for more concern and a celebration.

Dr. Colby immediately ordered that I be scheduled for a biopsy. Of course, I was excited about the possibility of getting some answers that might lead to my healing. I had grown weary so much speculating and people wanting to take shots in the dark at my expense. Some even wanted me to agree to having a surgeon cut me open to "look around and see if we can detect anything abnormal." They did not have a clue what was wrong with me. I was skeptical to say the least. Dr. Colby, (knowing all I had been through in search of answers, only to come back to him empty handed) understood my skepticism. He made arrangements in his orders for me to see both sets of x-rays prior to the surgery. However, his request was not honored. Instead the biopsy was scheduled and when the day arrived, they just came and took me down for surgery. Once again, I was challenged to speak up for myself.

When the nurse came in to explain the procedure and what was about to happen to me, she asked if I had any questions before signing my consent paperwork. I told her my doctor had requested I be shown the two sets of x-ray prior to surgery. She said "okay, I'll look into that" and left the room. Prior to the nurse returning to the room, the surgeon came in. He asked if the nurse had explained what the procedure entailed and if I was ready for the surgery. I told him the nurse had just left to follow up on Dr. Colby's orders that I see the x-rays prior to surgery. Feeling insulted, the surgeon became indignant. He asked me if I trusted him to do his job. I replied that was not the issue at all. I simply wanted to see and compare my x-rays prior to giving consent for the surgery. His pompous response then was "If you can't trust me to do my job, I am not touching you!" He proceeded to take off his surgical gear and walked out, leaving me lying on the operating table. When the nurse returned with no answers to my request and was told the surgeon had left, refusing to complete the surgery. I was returned to my room where I waited to inform Dr. Colby what had happened, knowing he would understand and respect my request to see the x-rays before signing the consent form.

After getting the opportunity to review my x-rays and making it clear to Dr. Colby that I did not want that surgeon to do the surgery, I signed the consent form.

Dr. Colby requested a transfer in his orders and referred me to Springfield to complete the biopsy. Being too weak to get to Springfield on my own, my youngest sister and best friend, Jeanette was my ride or die companion. Gin has always been my BFF, every since she could walk and talk she stayed right by my side. She recalls the story about her sitting in the waiting room at the hospital, waiting to take me home after the surgery. Before prepping me, the surgical medical team came out in full force to give her their prognosis. They noted that my labored breathing, coupled with how weak and thin I was, led them to believe I could not live through the procedure. They suggested she take time to call some more family members to be there with her when she received the bad news. They also allowed her to come in the room after they finished prepping me and say "Goodbye". According to Gin, she simply waited for the doctors to come out and let her go in to see me. They assumed she was going to say her goodbyes. Instead she came into the room, kissed me on the forehead and said "I'll see you when you get out". As the doctors prepared to leave the room to take me back for the surgery, they could not help but say "Mrs. Osler, you're handling this so well". She gave no response, just kept walking out of the room with the biggest smile on her face. She knew in her heart that my story was not going to end that way. Joining me in the recovery room was confirmation of her unwavering faith and belief that God would hear her prayers. This degree of confidence can only be attributed to the fact that we grew up watching our parents make a way out of no way and their explanation was always "God will give you a peace in times of trouble that no one can understand". The results were forwarded to Mayo Clinic.

When Dr. Colby received the results from Mayo Clinic, he rejoiced. He then told me he had suspected Sarcoidosis as a possibility and now it had been confirmed. He enthusiastically said, "alright Dorothy, now we can get to work. We are in this together". Armed with a specific diagnosis, Dr. Colby, immediately put together a team of well-respected specialists to join him in coordinating my treatment plan. He had great respect for their work and I trusted him and his judgement one hundred percent.

The Pulmonologist, Dr. Mauley, was chosen because of his vast experience with Sarcoidosis. Most specifically, he had worked extensively with a targeted group of 30 Black women all of whom had been diagnosed with Sarcoidosis. Dr. Mauley's role on the medical team was invaluable. He was very instrumental in helping me get a good handle on my acceptance of the diagnosis and the fact that so many would not understand what I would be going through. His excellent people skills made him the perfect choice for me. His calm, nurturing, reassuring demeanor was exactly what I needed, as I faced so many different challenges and unknowns on a daily basis. I had become extremely skeptical about everything and everybody. His considerable knowledge about Sarcoidosis coupled with his confidence was the security I needed. I felt very comfortable unloading my list of questions on him every time we met. Although he was always super busy, he never made me feel rushed or anxious about asking so many questions. Each answer just rolled off his tongue and oftentimes he would include additional information to help me get a better understanding. My confidence in his answers kept me at ease. Another bonus for me was he fit very nicely into the Dorothy and Dr. Colby Circle of Friends. He was never more than a telephone call away to address any issue that required his attention. Many times, he would personally return my call rather than his nurse.

Furthermore, I credit him with being one of the key players who inspired me to share my story. The love, respect and gratitude I have for him is immeasurable. He definitely has a seat at the table in my heart.

The Optometrist Dr. Colby brought to the team was also a perfect fit for me. It was immediately obvious that he had considered my personal level of need when choosing Dr. Sully who came with notable experience working with diseases of the eyes (his specialty). He, too had worked with a targeted group of patients with Sarcoidosis. In addition, his target group all had eye diseases associated with their diagnosis. Because of his expertise, he was already in great demand. He was successfully operating offices in two different cities, traveling around the world giving lectures and workshops, teaching and I suspect doing anything else that might allow him to share his knowledge and help people. The genuine concern and individualized care he gave me leads me to believe he had a special place in his heart for his Sarcoidosis patients.

While addressing the drastic change in my eyesight, he also treated me for the glaucoma and cataracts I inherited with my Sarcoidosis. I will be eternally grateful for his ability to head off the Glaucoma and save me from total blindness. With all due respect to Dr. Sully, I believed him when he said, in his opinion, the cataract surgery could wait; assuring me he would stay on top of it for any noted changes that might require the surgery be scheduled sooner rather than later. When talking about how I feel about my experience with Dr. Sully, I could actually ditto so much of what I said about Dr. Mauley. He was always one of my cheerleaders. His sincere compliments, encouragement and "Dorothy, did you write the book yet?" helped to fuel my desire to get my story told by finishing the book. Dr. Sully is another perfect addition to the Dorothy, Colby and Mauley Circle of Friends. He definitely has a seat at the table in my heart.

For me, both of these specialists were a great addition to my health care team. Together they were able to help Dr. Colby get me back on the road to stability and the quality of life I am able to enjoy today.

RESEARCH HERE I COME

"The Lord restoreth my soul for his name's sake. Yea, though I walked through the valley of the shadow of death, thy rod and thy staff comforted me. I feared no evil. The Lord, my God, was with me."

At this point, I want to invite others to share the Sarcoidosis experience by going back through my personal walk with Sarcoidosis. I am also sharing some of the information I have learned since being disabled by this incurable crippling disease. This reaffirms the reason I subtitled the book, What You Don't Know Could Kill You.

Psalms 23 has been an inspiration for me throughout my life and even more so during my times in the dark valley where Sarcoidosis took me. Accepting and adjusting to living with this painful and mysterious disease has been the biggest challenge I have ever faced in my life.

With a real diagnosis and sense of direction, my 'Need to Know More' neurons kicked in. I hit the ground running with the renewed strength I gained as a result of the Prednisone Dr. Colby prescribed for me. The increased appetite that accompanied Prednisone put some meat on my bones and I was able to get out of bed and be functional again.

I immediately began to research Sarcoidosis and share my diagnosis with others. I had so many questions, I did not know what direction to go in. I was in search of anyone who might have some knowledge of what challenges I may be facing. The responses ranged from those who actually had Sarcoidosis, some who knew someone who had it, to What Is Sarcoidosis? I was especially encouraged when I spoke to Sarcoidosis warriors who had been critically handicapped by the disease and were now in remission, reportedly having minimal discomfort and oftentimes no medication.

My first order of business was to get a definition that I could easily share with others when asked "what is that?" I needed to keep the definition simple so that I could answer that one question without opening the door to many more that I probably could not answer. So, I took pieces from different sources and put together the following definition:

Sarcoidosis (also at times referred to as Sarcoid): A chronic autoimmune system disease of unknown cause or cure. Characterized by producing tiny lumps of cells resembling little tumors primarily in the lungs but can move to other organs in the body. These clumps of cells come from the immune system and are also known as granulomas which can lead to death.

This definition has helped me to comfortably share my understanding of this mysteriously disabling disease while making no claim to have answers to lots of the questions that may follow. It continues to be challenging to get a good understanding of Sarcoidosis because it is so inconsistent. The fact that many of the symptoms overlap with other ailments make it difficult to even get a diagnosis of Sarcoidosis. What generally has to happen is a change occurs in the lungs which would necessitate a biopsy and possibly x-rays. For me, my lymph nodes were swollen. Others have reported their lungs shrunk.

After being diagnosed with Sarcoidosis, further testing may indicate it has invaded other organs in the body. The skin and eyes could also be affected. Should it enter the eyes, it could lead to either temporary or permanent blindness. While my eyesight is compromised, thanks be to God it still allows me to be independently functional.

Since so many test results come back negative, some warriors report having been treated for extended periods of time for such ailments as pneumonia, bronchitis and asthma and never getting any better. In many cases, their condition continually worsened, prior to getting the diagnosis of Sarcoidosis. Unfortunately, many warriors have lost the Sarcoidosis battle without even knowing they were in a fight, oftentimes mistakenly settling for the doctor saying "all tests are negative. Everything is fine."

The more I learned about the disease, the more I wanted to learn. When talking to others about the disease, Bernie Mac's name kept coming up as someone who had Sarcoidosis. I was told that complications with pneumonia and Sarcoidosis were the cause of his death in 2008.

Going on YouTube reading several posts about Bernie Mac and his Sarcoidosis experiences was not enough to satisfy my curiosity. It led me to explore the possibility of other Famous People who had been challenged by Sarcoidosis.

This list was obtained from Google (public access) at the time this book was written. Names are more than likely added regularly, in addition to many famous people going about their 'never you mind' with no clue they may have Sarcoidosis.

The following list includes famous people who are living with the disease and others who have passed away. I am not claiming to know whether or not any of the deaths resulted from Sarcoidosis, but feel if they had Sarcoidosis it complicated any other health issues they were battling.

Ada Sharpton	Al Sharpton's Mother
Angie Stone	Singer
Bernie Mac	Comedian and Actor
Bill Russell	Basketball Player
Charles P. Sifton	U.S. District Judge
Daisy Fuentes	TV Host and Model
Dale Armstrong	Race Car Driver
Darrell Hawks	Sports Anchor
Darrian Chapman	Sports Anchor
David McClendon	Journalist

Debbie Rowe	Model
Downtown Tina Brown	Actress/TV Personality
Evander Holyfield	Heavy Weight Boxing Champ
Floyd Mayweather, Sr.	Boxer and Trainer
James E. Ray	Basketball
Jason Horton	Basketball
Joseph Rago	Pulitzer Prize Winning Journalist
Judge Joe Brown	Honorable
Karen Duffy	Writer, Model and Actress
Karen Russell	Bill Russell's Daughter
King William Alexander	King of Netherlands
Mahalia Jackson	Gospel Singer
Manning Marable	Professor
Matthew Good	Musician
Michael Clark Duncan	Actor
Oji Pierce	Composer and Producer
Phillip Berrill	Artist and Author
Reggie White	Football Player
Ricky Dillard	Gospel Singer and Songwriter
Sean Lavert	Singer
Tinya Kerr (Mother)	Zach Kerr (NFL) Denver Broncos
Tisha Campbell	Actress
Travis Michael Holder	Actor/Playwright
Vickie Buckley	Former Secretary of State

There is speculation that William Shakespeare and Ludwig van Beethoven also had Sarcoidosis.

PERSONAL INTERVIEWS

Since being diagnosed with Sarcoidosis over 15 years ago, I have walked, talked, prayed with and interviewed many other warriors in my quest to know more. As a result, I have heard many stories and shared experiences that help enlighten others. I have spoken with Sarcoidosis sufferers from all different cultures, races, age groups and income levels. The group consisted of those who had only recently been diagnosed up to those who had battled over 30 years. Some shared stories of people they knew who had Sarcoidosis and passed away as a result. Others reported of people that passed away before the family ever got a true diagnosis. I wanted to share some of these interviews in the hope that my readers might get enough food for thought to inspire them to do more research and listen to their own body. There are some similarities in these interviews but many differences. I learned a great deal from each one of these interviews. Please note, some of the names have been changed in order to preserve the confidentiality of those who felt uninhibited when sharing their personal experiences with me.

Mister was one of the very first people I talked to in detail about my diagnosis. He was very eager to share his journey with me. We talked mostly about the different myths I was trying to sort through. My conversations with him helped give me a clearer picture of the direction I needed to take with my research. The most eye opening revelation Mister provided for me was dispelling the myth that Sarcoidosis was a "black woman's disease and usually attacked women between the ages of 20 to 40 years old". I had been told there was not a lot of specific information about

Sarcoidosis available and research was ongoing. I was led to believe that most doctors did not know very much about Sarcoidosis. He was living proof that the myth was far from truth because he had been living with Sarcoidosis for years. He added that he knew several others with Sarcoidosis, they did not fit into that grid. He knew of other men, white people, Asians and children. He noted that he knew of cases where doctors refused to consider looking at Sarcoidosis as a possibility for their white patients on the premise that it is a "Black disease". He was confident that in some of these instances, it cost the patient their life.

Mister told me he had been living with Sarcoidosis for "many years". His first warning signs were coughing, fatigue and labored breathing. He attributed his new quality of life to having an excellent medical team working with him. He was adamant about the importance of seeking out professionals who had specific experience with Sarcoidosis, noting that some professionals might attempt to treat me out of curiosity, but would not have any more knowledge about the disease than I had; which in the long run could very well do more harm than good. He encouraged me to follow my instincts and "do not hesitate to ask questions", reminding me that I owed it to myself. He stated that any care provider who could not address my concerns at a level of comfort I could live with should be relieved of the responsibility.

Also, if the recommended treatment from my doctor was not working, and I had to make repeated doctor visits for the same thing, I needed to move on and get another opinion. He made it clear to me that timing was everything and not moving on to someone who had experience treating Sarcoidosis patients could very well cost me my life.

Although I have not spoken with Mister for quite a while, when we last spoke he reported he was in remission. He was very happy to report he was continuing to enjoy a quality of life that allowed him to remain off Prednisone, exercise and walk on a regular basis without struggling. He continues to follow Sarcoidosis research and actively shares knowledge by networking with others. His testimony has encouraged me to do the same, in the hope that we might actually save or at least prolong some lives.

Another interview I want to share is Madam. Speaking with Madam periodically over many years has been an emotional roller coaster for me. Over the years, we have prayed, laughed, cried, testified, taught Sunday School together and anything we might feel like doing; which included some over the road trips. Although we have been personal friends for years, she never told me she had been living with Sarcoidosis long before I ever got my diagnosis. It wasn't until I asked her if she knew anything about Sarcoidosis that she shared her diagnosis with me. Since that time, she has been a wealth of support, information and encouragement. She has certainly been a factor in my decision to write a book that might be able to reach many more people than just word of mouth.

She, like me, always wants to know as much as possible about anything that challenges her like Sarcoidosis has. Madam has been battling Sarcoidosis for almost 20 years. She is one of the unfortunate ones that has to live with Sarcoidosis having settled in several organs throughout her body, bringing with it many other medical issues.

Madam was originally being repeatedly treated for pneumonia, bronchitis and COPD before Sarcoidosis was discovered in her lungs. Once diagnosed, she began aggressively researching the disease, noting any changes in her body so she could report them to her doctor. She soon discovered, as did I, that the inconsistencies and changes began to occur right away.

She subsequently contacted the Mayo Clinic with questions and was encouraged to come in for blood work. At the time of her arrival to the clinic her condition was so critical she was admitted. It was at that time she was informed the Sarcoidosis had also moved into her liver. As her journey continued, Sarcoidosis traveled into her kidneys and eyes. She has also experienced temporary blindness and a series of mini strokes. As she became increasingly concerned about the negative side effects attributed to prolonged use of Prednisone, she started to ask her doctor more questions. Not being comforted by the responses she received, depression began to resurface. Fueled by her frustration and dissatisfaction, she made the decision to travel to Southern Illinois University School of Medicine for a second opinion and additional testing.

In one of those appointments they explained to her that the normal "alkaline phosphatase" level for her should always be below 139. Yet, while she was being examined at the School of Medicine her alkaline phosphatase level was continually increasing; eventually getting beyond 900. Doctors cautioned her that her blood sugar was extremely high and suggested she allow them to admit her into the hospital in Springfield for further treatment. Madam said "no" and left there reassuring the doctors she would follow up with her Primary Care physician when she got back home. Subsequently, while driving herself back home, she started feeling sick and pulled off the highway so her son could complete the drive back home. Once back in town, her son took her directly to the Emergency Room where she was admitted. She then went into a diabetic coma. During this hospital stay she was told her extended use of Prednisone had destroyed her pancreas and she was now an insulin dependent diabetic. In addition, because of her pancreas being destroyed she was not a candidate for any pills. She was required to start with insulin shots immediately. She currently takes five (5) shots of insulin per day and still experiences "episodes" that hinder her quality of life on a regular basis. As a result of her blood sugar levels getting out of sync, she has also experienced blackouts.

With the disease originating in her lungs, Madam and I discussed many similar experiences we have had. When I told her about an increase in my inability to swallow and how frightening it is, she noted she still experiences these difficulties in spite of the fact that twice she has had her throat surgically stretched, two times so she could swallow. Though I have never undergone throat surgery, I was reminded of how far I have come from having to chew the flavor out of my food and spit the remains in the garbage.

Madam reported that after being diagnosed with Sarcoidosis she also developed a gum disease that required her to have all of her teeth removed. I shared with her that my teeth had become very brittle and began to chip off in tiny chunks that would get stuck in my throat. It became very serious because of the chance some of the small pieces would eventually block my throat and further compromise my ability to breathe and swallow. As a prevention, I had all my teeth surgically removed early on in my diagnosis.

Several of my most recent conversations with Madam have been bittersweet. At one point she answered the telephone very emotional stating she was "just very tired". She went on to say she had severed all ties with her doctors because they were not helping her. They had no answers for the incurable disease she had been struggling with all these years and none of the medication was working well enough to give her any real relief. In addition, her application for disability had been repeatedly denied, which added to her stress. I was very concerned about Madam's apathy and pleaded with her not to give up, offering any support I could possibly provide her while we prayed for her renewed strength.

During my most recent conversation with Madam, she reported she had re-established her relationship with her doctors and was back on her medication. She was in the process of reapplying for disability and was determined to remain optimistic. She went on to say some days were better than others and that through all her challenges she is keeping the Faith. Together we agreed 'To God Be The Glory'.

My third interview, with Cheryl was personally encouraging to me. Cheryl's symptoms and discomfort started in 1999, but it was not until 2001 that she was diagnosed with Sarcoidosis. She visited her primary care physician with questions and concerns about having a low grade temperature, a chronic cough, chest pains, chronic pain mainly in her ankles, weight loss and extreme fatigue. With all of these symptoms, her doctor began treating her for asthma. She went back and forth to the doctor to report she was getting very little relief in between visits. She continued to have the same concerns at each visit, but never left her doctor's office with any satisfactory answers that she felt comfortable with. Because her doctor had no real answers, he painted a very dismal picture for her. He tried to convince her that all her symptoms were just in her head. After completing chest x-rays, her primary care physician started treating her for pneumonia in an effort to address some of her complaints. Since there was still no improvement, she was told "it doesn't look good, you may not have long."

Cheryl eventually broke down into tears during a regularly scheduled office visit with her gynecologist. She shared with him how dissatisfied she was with her primary care physician who had been treating her for the same symptoms for months and was not helping her at all. She was getting no real answers, instead she was being led to believe there was no hope of ever getting better. Her gynecologist immediately ordered blood work and advised her there was something abnormal in her lungs. He referred her to a pulmonologist for further testing which included a biopsy. The test results indicated her lungs were shrinking and the diagnosis was Sarcoidosis.

She began a treatment plan that included an anti-inflammatory medication and prednisone. Her follow up plan includes annual x-rays and a pulmonary function test. She is now in remission, currently enjoying a quality of life with minimal discomfort, very little coughing, pain or compromised breathing. She is no longer on oxygen or any medications.

Cheryl said she learned two valuable lessons from her journey. It is important to be your own advocate, "nobody can do it better"; and, it is imperative to "stand on God's promises, by His strips we are Healed."

MY PERSONAL CHALLENGES

I have separated my challenges into two categories. There are major challenges that I wake up with and go to bed with every day. Those would be difficulty swallowing, breathing, coughing, chronic aches and pains. Then, I have short listed several challenges that come and go in varying degrees for variable periods of time. It should also be noted that I chose not to list some challenges that were too personal to share. First and foremost, I always feel exhausted. Some days are worse than others. There are times I feel too weak to get out of bed and my whole day consists of managing to get to the kitchen, bathroom and back to bed. This lack of energy always goes hand and hand with any of the other challenges I encounter.

One of my major challenges is difficulty swallowing. This has become a constant challenge for me. There is not a waking moment for me that I am not checking to see if my throat is working, to the point that when eating I feel the need to drink fluids in between bites in order to keep the food moving enough to get completely down my throat. There are still times the food will not make it and I have to take it back out. Other times I believe the food goes in the opposite direction and settles in my upper throat or somewhere behind my nose. As a result, I spend a lot of time hacking and coughing trying to dislodge hidden particles.

During the times I am not eating, in order to insure my throat does not forget to swallow, I constantly suck mints and lozenges, or keep the liquids flowing. This daily ongoing routine keeps me very anxious because I live with the fear of this not being enough at some point. Many times this experience creates enough stress to jumpstart the dry coughing which generally causes a very sore throat. Adding another layer of pain I have to live with.

Overall, the energy required to get food into my system makes the whole eating exercise unenjoyable. I eat very small portions of food when I do eat just to keep my frustration level down. I have actually given up one of my favorite foods (popcorn), among others because of the challenge.

With swallowing being a challenge, saliva builds up in my mouth and won't go down my throat; instead it just settles until I manually clean it out in order to prevent uncontrollable coughing or choking. Another scary challenge for me is my struggle to breath. Generally minimal walking or talking compromises my breathing. On a bad day, this can even include going from room to room in the house. As a result, I do a lot of sitting down, and getting up. There are many days

I am not even able to leave home. Once that happens, I begin coughing. This affects my ability to talk or swallow. The anxiety from this starts my rapid heartbeat and sweats. The list goes on.

Upon discharge from the hospital, after my second bout with double pneumonia. and an extended stay in Intensive Care, I was still not breathing completely on my own. Dr. Colby's resolution for this challenge was to send me home with supplemental oxygen that was supposed to be temporary, "until my lungs were able to build back up." However, I have not yet been able to get back to independent breathing. Currently, my level of breathing comfort depends on my oxygen use.

My progress is monitored on a regular basis by Dr. Mauley during my visits. Each time I am required to disconnect completely from the oxygen and walk around with a pulsometer on my finger. The nurse monitors my internal oxygen level which has consistently decreased when not supplemented by external oxygen. In fact, the results from my most recent Pulmonary Function test indicated a progressive decrease in my lung capacity.

Another major challenge would be the constant coughing which I am very happy to say is nowhere near as bad as it used to be. I attribute this mainly to my consistent conscious effort to minimize my stress level which plays a major role in my coughing. Some days are better than others. There are times I cough so much I become lightheaded. This experience is very scary and forces me to immediately shut down and sit down until I am stable again. My heart rate increases, I begin shaking and then comes the hot and cold flashes. During this panic attack, I can feel my throat closing more and more which also increases my anxiety.

The following list includes several challenges I have lived with more often than not throughout this journey. Some people reading this list can only imagine the different challenges, but you can't make this stuff up. I do know that anyone suffering with the chronically disabling disease Sarcoidosis, will be able to identify with many of these harsh realities. I am sure many of my Sarcoidosis sisters and brothers would be able to add other challenges to this list.

The inflammatory muscle and joint pains either wake me up in the early mornings or keep me up most nights. Not one day is pain free. Some days I hurt so bad I cannot hold back the tears. Many times the pain is so crippling, it makes me immobile and I am not able to get out and about at all until my relief comes. There are times Charley Horses accompany the joint pains. They can be so intense in my calves I don't think my leg will ever straighten out again.

Sometimes my hands ache so bad I cannot even open a pull tab on a can of tuna or snap open a sandwich bag. There are days my shakes and aches are so bad that I celebrate just successfully putting an ice tray in the freezer without having to mop the floor.

Some days I wake up with bruises on my body that look like I got in a fight and lost. They are generally on my legs but do appear in other places from time to time.

The numbness that randomly moves around in my body is so unsettling to me because I never know which body parts might not work. At any moment, it might start in my feet and fingers then end up in my face and arms. I may be in the middle of a project or conversation and the numbness will just short circuit me. These occurrences often bring me to tears. It's like an out of body experience that I have no control over.

Depending on what medications I take, my weight very often fluctuates. There are days I can choose to wear anything in my closet and other days I might have to try on several different pieces to see what fits.

There are times my ears go into airplane mode and pop as if I am in an airplane. Then, there are occasions when just trying to engage in conversation, talk on the telephone, watch a movie, or simply get through the day can be challenging. This because all the while I am hearing popcorn popping in my ears. The slow steady popping noise is a total distraction and there is no time limit on how long it will go on. At times, it even interrupts me when I am reading or trying to sleep. There are times my equilibrium is affected by the popping and I am afraid to stand up for fear of falling.

Although I used to love a dark, quiet room, now I choose never to sleep in pitch darkness because I have difficulty focusing because there are bunches of little multi-colored circles going all around the room, bringing back memories of my college partying days when strobe lights were the thing. I am certainly not feeling the same about this experience these days. I would have to agree with B.B. King and say, 'The Thrill is Gone'. I attribute this challenge to the glaucoma and cataracts associated with my Sarcoidosis.

There are times I have little dry, itchy patches show up randomly, generally on my hands or face. These patches just add to my already the extremely flaky dry skin that I inherited as a result of my Sarcoidosis. My nose is also a challenge. There are days when it runs so much I am wiping and sneezing constantly. Other times, during the same day, my nose might get so dry it hurts for me to wipe it. Many times it will start bleeding, for no apparent reason. Any or all of these challenges might occur, any time of the day or night, without notice – no warning.

Relocating to another state, was a major adjustment for me and my Sarcoidosis. The new environment and climate change came with a whole new set of challenges. Nevertheless, I have been blessed with another primary care physician (Dr. Gladney) who treats me like his favorite child.

He respects my need to know personality and is always patient with me. He allows me to get each of my questions and concerns addressed. He is a wealth of information, not only with regard to Sarcoidosis. He stays abreast of current research and resources, including holistic treatments. He fits in perfectly with my Dream Team and has already earned a seat at the table in my heart.

During my initial appointment with Dr. Gladney, we were able to cover a lot of the challenges I just listed, many of which he was able to address in the medical treatment plan he developed for me. He increased my Ipratropium Bromide and Albuterol Sulfate inhaler solution treatments to four (4) times a day. In addition to the Metformin I am already taking, he added four (4) new prescriptions. In addition, he included a list of natural herbs in the plan. Each of the new medications have their own set of side effects; creating even more challenges for me. The changes to my health plan have proven to be a plus for me. The level of comfort I enjoy with my breathing has increased. Some days are better than others. Although the insomnia still haunts me, when I do sleep, the quality has significantly improved. The additional breathing treatments and medications have reduced my stress level to the point that I am able to enjoy an overall higher quality of life. There are still some times I opt to sleep sitting up, in order not to get so relaxed and comfortable that my throat might forget to swallow.

STRESS CAN KILL YOU

I believe the biggest challenge Sarcoidosis presents is stress. While Sarcoidosis comes with its own set of challenges and there is no cure for it, not managing your stress level can be fatal. I have taken the time to detail a near death experience for me that changed my life and forced me to re-prioritize the things important enough for me to choose life. I share this in the hopes that my story might help prevent someone else from letting their guards down when dealing with stress, leaving the door open for Sarcoidosis to come in and have its way in their life.

I would also like to take this opportunity to note that Sarcoidosis or not, excess stress and worry can take anyone's life. The firsthand experience that forced me to see exactly what stress coupled with depression, can do came when my youngest brother, Joey, passed away unexpectedly. I knew as I walked out of the hospital, I was going into a dark place. I could not imagine life without my baby brother. The shock of his death kicked off a Sarcoidosis episode that I really did not believe I would survive. As the walls closed in around me, I alone could not save myself.

Joey and I were joined at the hip. He was my Go-To brother. Because of my health challenges, he stepped up to the plate to help me care for our Father. He would drive me and dad to all of our appointments in and out of town. He wanted to be able to provide any assistance we needed. Although some of my days were better than others, he never wanted me to go to my appointments alone. He always took time off work for any appointments I or Dad had. In fact, there were times I was too weak to walk into my own appointments and Joey would cradle me in his arms and carry me like a little baby. Most times, because of my chronic cough, he would then have to do most of the talking. Oftentimes he would laughingly say, "Dorothy, just let me talk. We'll be in here all day." I loved him so much.

Although Joey had his own personal health issues, he never let us down. He knew how much it bothered me to be dependent on others, rather than being the caregiver, so he never complained, regardless of our level of need. There were times he would come to pick our father up for an appointment and while walking around to open the door for me he would say "Dorothy, you sicker than Dad, where you goin'?" He made it easy to take our minds off our pain and suffering because he kept us laughing the whole time we traveled up and down the highway. Just being in his company and feeling the genuine love and concern he had for me and Dad, I would often try to say "Thank You" but the tears would start to flow and the coughing would not let me finish my sentence. While fighting back his own tears, Joey would say "Aww, Dorothy, stop cryin' girl it's alright. That's what I'm here for." I just knew our bond was unbreakable. Then death came and just snatched away the one person who had promised to always be there for me. I had been at Joey's bedside 24 hours a day for 20 days while he laid there in what the doctors called a "coma". When the doctors said "He's gone." I was so devastated, I couldn't move. I didn't believe he was really gone. I honestly believed he would always be there for me as he had promised when our Father passed away. On that cold January day, my whole world got darker.

Having the compromised immune system with Sarcoidosis would not allow me to muster up any resistance to fight off the deep depression taking over my mind and body. I could not wrap my mind around the fact that my baby brother was gone. He was so full of life and I had been so sick and suffering for years. I could not find any peace with Joey's life being cut that short and I was still here.

The point I want to make with such a detailed story is how important it is for us Warriors to always keep in mind what Sarcoidosis is capable of doing if you let your guards down. I am thankful that I lived to share my experience because after leaving the hospital I went home and spiraled down into a valley of doom. I am not sure exactly how long I just laid in my apartment not eating, drinking, sleeping, answering the telephone or door. I did not even take any medication. I just laid there, questioning God and wondering what was taking the Death Angel so long to come and claim me. At some point I tried to get out of bed and passed out in my apartment. That's where my sons found me and took me to live with my oldest son, Richard and wife Alisia along with four (4) of my grandchildren. I stayed with them for several months.

When my faith in God returned, I could surely see His hand in this whole experience. It was during my hiatus at my son's house that my will to keep living was restored. Living with my grandchildren, and having the others visit regularly, helped me to heal inside. Their sincere love and concern nurtured me back to where I needed to be in order to adopt the Serenity Prayer and accept the things I cannot change, to have the courage to change the things I can and to possess the wisdom to know the difference.

I left my son's house with a firm determination not to let Sarcoidosis block my blessings, coupled with a renewed commitment to let God have His way in my life. He is the potter; I am the clay. It was at this point I was convinced God kept me here because He was not finished answering my prayers, especially allowing me to be able to share this experience with others and possibly save lives.

WE ARE FAMILY – I'LL BE THERE

Throughout this journey, God removed from my life some key players who were solid bricks in my foundation. However, those of us remaining continue to be strong. I have lived long enough to realize that God's ways and plans for my life are always better than my own and everything in my life is working together for my good.

I continually thank God for the family he blessed me with, particularly my siblings. I am often overwhelmed with emotions just thinking about how much we love each other. Each of my siblings have remained steadfast in their support of me, individually and collectively throughout my highs and lows. The love and bond between me and my siblings makes it impossible to share my journey without intertwining them throughout the book. I carry them in my heart and prayers always.

Cherishing some of my fondest memories, while thanking God for His grace and mercy brings to mind my father telling me that when I was too sick to take care of myself he was concerned I would stop breathing at any time. So, every night he would pull a chair up beside my bed and sit there all night watching me struggle to breath because he wanted to be right by my side when I took my last breath. Something he told us he did for his mother who died with pneumonia when he was only 13 years old. Hmm??? She might have had a case of undiagnosed Sarcoidosis. Research indicates it can be hereditary.

Another cherished memory I hold near and dear to my heart is my relationship with my big sister, Judy. Who we fondly called Ms. Davis. She consumes much more than a small pocket in my heart. Her love and concern for me played a major role in saving my life. I can remember one of my all time lows, when I really struggled just to get out of bed and put one foot before the other. Ms. Davis brought Darin and me into her house to stay. During those days she would wash me, comb my hair and feed me while we listened to gospel music, looked at old family pictures and watched videos. We both loved to sit at the table in her living room and look out her big picture window most of the day, just watching the people walking past and traffic going back and forth.

When she would put me down to bed, she always insisted that I lay with my back up against hers so she could feel me breathing throughout the night. Many times we would lay awake late into the night talking about our aches, pains, prayers, dreams and memories.

It was during one of those bonding moments that Ms. Davis revisited my request that she be there for my son,

Darin, should I not make it. She insisted I not stress about anything. She shared with me a letter she had written for Darin, insuring him she would be there for "us". She never even entertained the thought that I might not make it.

After mother passed away, Ms. Davis was the matriarch in our family. So many of us would regularly sit at her table for guidance and inspiration. She never missed an opportunity to tell and show everyone how much she loved them. I thank God for letting my big sister live long enough to see her many prayers for me answered. She was able to witness me having a reasonable portion of my health restored and an improved quality of life.

She never missed an opportunity to tell each of us how much she loved us while insisting on getting hugs and kisses from everybody, even the friends that might have come with us.

I watched her overcome so many of her own challenges while remaining ready and willing to stand in the gap to nurture so many other people. She was wise way beyond her years and was a source of comfort and consolation to many. Ms. Davis was really one of my biggest inspirations to live. Not only did I watch her fight a good fight while dealing so many of her own health challenges, she was the key player in getting me to take the first step towards my own recovery.

Over the years, she looked death in the face so many times in her life while battling many different medical problems and getting no real answers from doctors. Many of them gave her no signs of hope or encouragement. She literally traveled all over the country searching for answers to the many different symptoms and daily challenges she experienced throughout her body. Every time she returned home from a doctor's visit she had a different diagnosis but no cure. Several times, doctors just threw up their hands saying there was nothing else they could do they recommended Hospice. To my knowledge, the possibility of Sarcoidosis was never explored. Hmm, could she have been a victim of "What You Don't Know, Could Kill You"?

Needless to say, it was devastating for me when Ms. Davis transitioned into Glory while peacefully sleeping. This time, Sarcoidosis did not ruin my ability to celebrate her life and enjoy her Homegoing Celebration. Since God resurrected me from the pits of depression after Joey's death, I continue to hold fast to the Serenity Prayer by minimizing my stress and being determined to never give Sarcoidosis control over my life again.

Not enough can be said about my big sister, Beulah, (Dr. Lateef). She has always been, and still is my She-ro. Her loving, caring nurturing of me contributes a great deal to my ability to remain physically and mentally stable. She has always shouldered up with me to carry my burdens. My challenge with Sarcoidosis was no different. The very beginning of my diagnosis was the most difficult time period for me because there were no answers as I continued to lose ground. During those times, when I fell (sometimes literally) and just couldn't get up, that Beulah would be standing there with her hand extended. Her shoulder has been there for me my entire life and still is. With her nursing experience, she stayed on top of any of the medical assessments and the recommendations I received. She was my personal interpreter, translator and advocate.

Beulah never let her own busy, complicated life slow her roll. She always made time to be there for me and my needs while being there for so many others. In the midst of teaching classes at a university, traveling to do speaking engagements, conducting workshops and Reading Recovery training for Teacher Leaders, she raised four (4) children as a single parent. She also managed to drive to Illinois at least two times a week and most weekends to help take care of both me and our Father. There were many times she would just sit and cradle me in her arms and I would tearfully thank her for all she did. Very much in line with 'Footprints' she would repeat a phrase we grew up hearing our Mom and Dad say to so many, "Thank God I was able".

My younger sister, Sennie, (Dr. Smith) was also a very present contributor to my ability to worry about nothing, except getting better. Minimizing my stress level and avoiding Sarcoidosis spin downs was one of her top priorities. Whenever she was home from Germany, she would ride side saddle with Joey to help take care of me and Dad. Although she lived and worked in Germany, she respected my wishes to "Give me my flowers while I yet live so I could smell them". Our mother always said that throughout her life. She loved fresh flowers and plants. Sennie made sure I always had fresh flowers delivered to my hospital room and later to my door. She still surprises me with flower deliveries from time to time, for no specific occasion. In addition, during my hospital stays, Sennie would call several times a day to get status reports from hospital staff. She also made some of her calls during the evening so she could speak directly with Dr. Colby. She did continual research and always had plenty questions, suggestions and recommendations.

Her conversations with me were generally motivational. She prayed with me while urging me to keep the faith and give God the glory for allowing me to live. She would assure me that my trials and tribulations would only make me stronger, "No Test, No Testimony". She was convinced God had a great work for me to do. Ironically, she always thought it would be writing a book and sharing these experiences with others. She has always been relentless with her encouragement and support.

LEAN ON ME – THAT'S WHAT FRIENDS ARE FOR

I am sure many of my readers can remember when I was just skin and bones, having lost over one hundred pounds. My lowest weight from the 277 pounds I weighed before getting a diagnosis and treatment plan was when I weighed only 98 pounds. Many who were in my company at the onset of the Sarcoidosis might also recall my chronic cough and struggling to breathe. Though there was no way they could have known how sick I really was, so many still reached out to help me. I continue to be a firm believer that it takes a village to stand in the gap for us Warriors having to deal with the challenges of Sarcoidosis. I am tremendously blessed to have such a continually growing village. Some have come for a season, others stepped up and never left my side, always just a telephone call away. In fact, many still maintain regular contact with me, just checking to see how I'm doing.

I firmly believe that God sprinkled these seeds all along my life's path, even before my Sarcoidosis diagnosis. One or more of them always sprout up just when I need them most.

My sincere desire to acknowledge and thank these supporters, was initially a dilemma for me. I actually struggled with how I could make this group of people know what they have meant to me, and how eternally grateful I am for the role they have played in my village. Initially, I wanted to name each of them individually, but, since there are so many I could not risk the possibility of leaving not even one name off the list. It would truly break my heart if that were to happen. As a solution, I fondly pinned the name "Angel Seeds" to a list I carry in my heart and for the purposes of this book. I know it is not possible for me to get to each one of my Angel Seeds individually to say "Thank You". But I do believe I will have the opportunity to autograph a book for many of them.

There were many times I was too sick to even recognize or remember the hands that reached out to help me, and the list continues to grow on a daily basis. I am sure God is keeping an up to date list of my angels and I have asked Him to bless them for me.

Another source of inspiration for me has been the online Support Groups I recently joined. The whole experience and involvement has been a tremendous blessing for me. The ability to network with other Sarcoidosis Warriors has been enriching. The experience has proven to be a very big piece of the puzzle I have been working on since being diagnosed. They have been company keepers for me during the times I could not get out and about because of excruciating aches, pain and other physical challenges I've had to deal with during any particular time. My interaction with other Warriors allows me to realize I am not alone and to look at the glass as half full rather than half empty. There are so many others out there who are willing to share their experiences. This keeps me thankful and optimistic. Being a part of these groups adds another layer of family to my rich legacy. From the very beginning I was welcomed into the group. Although I do not always agree with everyone and everything, I have been made to feel very comfortable sharing. I share my mood swings, aches, pains, questions and findings. I get a chance to vent to sympathetic ears who can relate to my struggles. It is understood within the Sarcoid family that the only 'stupid question' is one that never gets asked. We are all learning from each other. The combined shared knowledge is invaluable, opening doors to conferences, new research, additional resources, and many other Warriors at different stages of their journey.

This group involvement allows me to see a much broader picture of Sarcoidosis and a full spectrum of its effects on many different individuals.

It is such a comfort to be able to converse on a 24/7 basis with others who are as close as it gets to understanding what I am experiencing. The genuine compassion, concern and bond developed through the groups interaction is priceless.

Although no two journeys are the same, there is a common thread running through the hearts of the Warriors in our group. I feel up-close and personal with them; and I have no reservations sharing my joys, questions, fears, doubts, emotions and good or bad news. Some individuals in the group (not all) reach out regularly and communicate. I am always able to link up with those who are good listeners, patient, responsive, encouraging, nonjudgmental and will pray with me and for me.

My group involvement allows me to feed my need-to-know and need-to-share bug. There is always at least one other person online willing to respond regardless of what time of day or night it is. The Support Group is fertile ground for venting about my challenges and frustrations in dealing with such a crippling disease, with no cure in sight. In addition, I always have someone to celebrate praise reports with me. Lastly, the groups have afforded me the opportunity to fulfill my insatiable desire to help others and the freedom to continue social working by sharing my personal challenges and the knowledge I have gathered along the way.

I would certainly encourage anyone that has been diagnosed with Sarcoidosis, has someone in their family with the diagnosis, or lost someone with it to join a Support Group. I promise you will not regret it. The benefits will be immeasurable.

THE SOUND OF MUSIC – MUSIC THERAPY

Reading and music have always been my passion; I find inspiration in good music and good books. I can easily get into a place of tranquility by internalizing the words and letting them nurture me. With my eyesight now being compromised as a result of the Sarcoidosis, music has been my main source of tranquility. Music provides another layer of protection for me when situations appear to be getting too stressful.

Following is a condensed list of my 'Go To' songs and artists. I pray some of my readers might find a way to listen to selections from this list that might bless them with the peace I have enjoyed.

Amazing Grace	Al Green
And You Don't Stop	The Walls Group
Because You Loved Me	Celine Dion
Changed	Tremaine Hawkins
Close	Marvin Sapp
Dear God	Smokie Norful
Encourage Yourself	Donald Lawrence
For Your Glory	Tasha Cobb
Grace and Mercy	Mississippi Mass Choir
Grateful	Hezekiah Walker
He Has His Hands on You	Marvin Sapp
How Great Thou Art	Yolanda Adams
I Almost Gave Up	Kurt Carr
I Can Only Imagine	Tamela Mann
I Look to You	Whitney Houston
I Need You to Survive	Hezekiah Walker
I Understand	Smokie Norful
I Won't Complain	Angie Stone
If Nothing Else, Thank You	Saints With A Vision
In the Midst of It All	Yolanda Adams
Lean on Me	Kirk Franklin
Let the Church Say Amen	Andrea Crouch
Lord Give Me You	Shana Wilson
Marvelous	Walter Hawkins
Never Would Have Made It	Marvin Sapp
No Greater Love	Smokie Norful
Nobody Greater	Vashawn Mitchell
Safe in his Arms	Rev. Milton Brunson
Smile	Kirk Franklin
That's When He Blessed Me	L A Mass Choir
The Battle is not Yours	Yolanda Adams
Trust in You	Anthony Brown
We Must Praise	J. Moss
Worth	Anthony Brown

INSPIRATION

Hopefully by sharing my story other lives will be saved. Prayerfully by reading something within these pages others will be motivated to not only be more attentive to their body's language, but also to more carefully watch over others they know and love. I shutter to think where I might be had I accepted "well Dorothy, all your lab work was negative. Everything looks good." I could have gone back home, still experiencing the same discomfort and confusion and never getting an explanation as to why and what could be done.

It is important to keep in mind that since there are so many different possibilities for what might be contributing to changes in your body, you have to become more involved.

This requires getting very familiar with your personal self and keeping good notes to go over during doctor visits. Always keep in mind there is no such thing as a 'stupid' question. Do not hesitate to ask anything. You owe it to yourself; and it could be a matter of life or death.

There were times I had different aches, pains and discomfort every day but minimized it. Please don't do as I did, do as I say. Had my body not completely shut down, landing me in Intensive Care, fighting for my life, I could have been in the number of others who died on the vine before getting into a treatment plan that might have saved their life. It is my hope that the information readers get from this book will only scratch the surface. That it will peak their curiosity and generate more questions, moving them to do more research on their own. I hope that they continue to share anything they learn with others, creating a snowball effect that will not stop moving.

Prayerfully, sharing my personal journey and triumphs will be encouraging enough to restore hope and faith to many who may have contemplated giving up. I continue to have many trials and tribulations but hold fast to the belief that I, too, will be blessed to experience the wonders of remission, maybe even a cure during my lifetime. Only God's grace kept me. I remind myself of this often by revisiting one of the passages from Mary Stevenson's poem 'Footprints' when God said, "My precious child, I would never leave you during your time of trial. When you see only one set of footprints, it is then that I carried you."

DON'T CHARGE IT TO THE HEART

Those of you who know me personally already know I have 'Easy Feelings'. It does not take much for me to drop a tear. Which is why I decided to provide a short list of some very painful remarks that have been made during my journey. Many of these have been said to me and some reported to me by other Warriors. I am sure this list is not complete and new ones can be added everyday by other Warriors.

You don't even look sick.
You're lying.
I don't believe you.
It's not that bad.
You're exaggerating.
You just want the attention.
Nobody can be that sick all the time.
You tired already?
You're just lazy.

Why don't you just get a shopping cart and go get what you need.
Get some therapy, that's just in your head.
You just need to exercise more.
All you need to do is give up Pepsi and change your diet.
You just don't want to get better.
You need to stop taking all that medicine and go holistic.
You always complaining.
Just keep walking, I parked right over there.
I just sprayed a little, it's not that bad.
Yes. I'm sick, but you're not going to catch anything.
Maybe you should just lose some weight.
I'm taking this parking space, you can walk that, it's not very far.
This smoke won't bother you, just turn your back.

Several of these comments may sound familiar to some of you because they have probably rolled off your tongue on occasion. While I certainly would not charge it to anyone's heart because I assume they do not know enough about Sarcoidosis to realize their flippant remarks are hurtful to someone suffering with Sarcoidosis. That being said, it is my prayer that those reading this book will take the lead in reducing the occurrence of these hurtful remarks. When you know better, you should do better. By sharing this information with others, you can now play a major role in sparing someone who is already dealing with their own share of pain any unnecessary additional pain.

I CAN ONLY IMAGINE

"God uses ordinary people to do extraordinary things"

When I look back over my life, most specifically the past 15 years, I ask myself "How do I say thanks for the things God has done for me?" I have asked God to enlarge my territory and use me for His glory, that I might be a beacon of hope and encouragement for others, using any time I have remaining in this life to be a big part of enriching the lives of others. The completion of this book will definitely not be the end of my sharing. I will continue to support and network, my motive always being to possibly save the lives of others while continuing my commitment to myself I want to make the rest of my life the best of my life, (Louise Hay)

Being the dreamer that I am, John Lennon recorded it perfectly in his song "Imagine: You may say I'm a dreamer, but I'm not the only one. I hope someday others will join me."

Just a couple of the things I imagine are very possible: That I may prayerfully be in a position to help support others in their struggles. This would involve developing teams of support specialists to travel around the country setting up and organizing individual Sarcoidosis support groups.

Some specific objectives would be to provide emotional support to those Warriors struggling with accepting the challenges associated with Sarcoidosis. I also want to cultivate information exchanges and nurturing support for individuals that have lost loved ones to Sarcoidosis. At the same time, I want to motivate groups to continually develop and define new objectives. Secondly, another dream would be to coordinate a (1-800) telephone support line that would be available to warriors and anyone else wanting a nonjudgmental listening ear while addressing questions, concerns and specific needs. The objective would be to enrich and enhance the quality of life for others. Aside from being staffed with good listeners, supporters would include physicians, counselors, coordinators, warriors, other professionals and service providers.

In addition, physicians and health care providers would be able to refer patients and clients to the line for additional support and guidance

CONCLUSION

Writing this book was very hard for me at times because it forced me to re-live some very painful memories. However, it was in many ways bittersweet because I am reminded of how really sick I was and able to reflect on the quality of life I am able to enjoy now.

I know God's timing is not ours. I am so incredibly thankful that He restored my health enough to allow me to be able to resume taking care of my father and his needs until he took his last breath. I was able to give back some of the loving nurturing care he had given me.

When I look back over my life and all I have been through to get to where God has brought me, I know it is with purpose. I have never believed in coincidences and am convinced God is using me to do His will through the writing of this book. I have heard it said and I believe it, "God puts us in the right place, at the right time, with the right people so he can work His will for us in our lives."

Throughout my life and career, I have always postured myself to stand in the gap for others. This illness is no different. It is my heart's desire to gather and share any information I may acquire, in the hopes of saving or enlightening others who may not be able to do the work for themselves, those who may not even be aware of their need to know.

I honestly believe that as people read through the pages of this book, whether having Sarcoidosis or not, they will feel my joy and pain. For those with Sarcoidosis it is my prayer that the sharing of my personal journey and triumphs will be encouraging enough to restore hope and faith. Throughout my walks and talks with other Warriors some of the painfully sad statements I have heard are:

"I'm so tired."
"I can't do this any more."
"Why don't God just take me?"
"I'm in the hospital again. Don't know if I'll be going back home."
"Maybe I just won't wake up tomorrow."
"I have no good days."
"I just quit taking all my meds. It's not helping anyway. I'm just getting worse."
"There's no cure, so what difference does it make,"

Admittedly, I still have some days when I am sick and tired of being sick and tired, but I am determined to accept the things I cannot change and continue to trust God for my health and strength. I pray God use me as a living testimony to others who may be ready to give up. God is answering my prayer through the completion of this book. My contribution to those Warriors that might be growing weary of this crippling disease that has no cure.

One of my favorite poems:

"Don't Quit"
When things go wrong, as they sometimes will,
When the road you're trudging seems all uphill,
When the funds are low and the debts are high,
And you want to smile, but you have to sigh,
When care is pressing you down a bit,
Rest, if you must, but don't you quit.
Life is queer with its twists and turns,
As every one of us sometimes learns,
And many a failure turns about,
When he might have won had he stuck it out;
Don't give up though the pace seems slow–
You may succeed with another blow.
Often the goal is nearer than
It seems to a faint and faltering man,
Often the struggler has given up,
When he might have captured the victor's cup,
And he learned too late when the night slipped down,
How close he was to the golden crown.
Success is failure turned inside out–
The silver tint of the clouds of doubt,
And you never can tell how close you are,
It may be near when it seems so far,
So stick to the fight when you're hardest hit–
It's when things seem worst that you mustn't quit.
- Author Unknown -

God never promised you it would be easy, he did promise he would never leave you. Please know if you are still here, he is not finished with you yet.

ACKNOWLEDGEMENTS

First and foremost, I give God total praise. I thank Him for my life, family and friends. All that He has done, is doing and will do for me. He is the beginning and end of everything I am. His Grace and tender mercy allows me to Fly Without Wings and soar above and beyond my greatest imagination.

These acknowledgements of gratitude may seem extensive to some, but I have actually condensed my list. I realize that the challenges of Sarcoidosis do truly continue to take a village. I would be remiss not to note some of the people who were footprints in the sand for me.

Without reservation, I firmly believe anything I have and will accomplish has to be attributed to the foundation set by my parents, R E and LeeAnnie Goines. They always took time to affirm that each one of us were wanted and considered to be a gift from God. Although my mother only completed fourth grade and my father seventh grade, they were clever enough to instill a sense of purpose, pride and conviction in all of their children.

Education and giving back by paying forward were core values in our family. We were all always encouraged to take advantage of any opportunity to learn anything we could and share it with others. As a family, we always had ongoing Round Table Level 5 discussions. We talked about anything that hit the table. My parents were right in the middle of all of it. Oftentimes, other family members, neighbors and friends came through and participated. This piece of our legacy continues to live on in different family homes.

I offer undying recognition to my Medical Dream Team who blessed me with a quality of life that I would not have believed possible, considering where I was and the challenges we faced.

Dr. Colby, who is now retired, was my power source when I was dying on the vine. I am sure his threat to call the morgue if I did not leave his office and go directly to the hospital saved my life. Although he apologized later for some of the language he used with me, I never charged it to his heart. I know it was just tough love.

His relentless pursuit for answers to why I was so sick and his genuine concern for my well-being validates why choosing him to be my primary care physician was a no brainer.

I recognize Dr. Mauley for his nurturing care during my hospital stay and his continuing care over the years. He encouraged me to not only learn as much as I can about the disease for myself, but to share my personal experiences with others. He often complimented me on my positive attitude and handling of the challenges brought on by Sarcoidosis.

Dr. Sully shared with me very early during our appointments how impressed he was with my thirst for knowledge. He suggested I "write a book" and agreed to be my mentor should I make the decision. He has been consistently supportive and encouraging, noting that although each person's experience would be different, he was confident my story would serve as a valuable point of reference to others during their journey. I am sure, with that in mind, he always took the time during our visits to answer the list of questions I had prepared to further my research.

Dr. Roberson, was actually my father's doctor. He was aware of my health challenges and always genuinely concerned about me. He exhibited concern and compassion, always asking me if I had any questions he might be able to address for me. He was more than willing to share his medical knowledge and research with me.

Dr. Gladney, my current primary care physician, has been a great addition to the medical support team that took care of me for the past 15 years. He is very knowledgeable about Sarcoidosis and the treatment plan he set up with me certainly contributed to the quality of life I currently enjoy.

My brother in-law, Jasper Osler, Jr. was and is one of my ride or die sidekicks. He stands shoulder to shoulder with my sister, Jeanette, poised and ready to do anything needed. Realizing the impact of Joey's death on me, he stepped up his game by willingly standing in the gap. Actually, Jasper continues to be on post for me. Literally just a phone call away.

I have two amazing sisters in-love, Catherine and Chris Goines, both of whom I will refer to as "die hards" because individually they are eveready. There was never a time that I called either of them and they did not come. They were always willing to help support me in my struggle to regain a reasonable portion of my health and strength.

Jacqueline Ward, one of my dearest friends and a former coworker, knowing I was too sick to take care of myself or my son, Darin, extended the invitation for us to come stay in her home with her and her son, Jarin. During this time, she treated Darin as if he were her own child, making sure all of his needs were met. She made sure he got to school, afterschool programs, basketball practice and games. She took care of his lunch money and any other needs as they arose. At the same time, she made sure I was comfortable and taken care of. She would even make arrangements to bring my grandson, Terryn, for extended visits with me. Her kindness will never be forgotten.

If anyone could see the dictionary of words I carry in my heart they would see beside the words "true friend"

Jacqueline Ward's name on the list. Throughout the subsequent years, whenever our paths cross, I continue to thank her for having been such a blessing to me and my son. It is an honor to have her say "Dorothy, I know you would have done the same thing for me".

Special recognition to my Muslim family who also contribute to my village. To name a few: Aishah Akbar, Deonte and Amira Saleem (and kids), Sameerah Akbar and Safiyyah Rahim. They stand ready and willing to help in any way they can.

CREDITS

Editing	Dr. Beulah Lateef Dr. Jeanette Osler Dr. Sennie Smith
Consultation	Dezera R.B. Davis Alisia Goines Christine Goines T. Bone Goines Quan Lateef-Hill Reanna Osler Edie Purdy Safiyyah Rahim
Technical Support	Angela Goines Vaneitta Goines Jasper Osler III Makeda Osler Xavier Osler Jason Smith
Transporters	Aishah Akbar Maryka Osler Deonte Saleem
Dispatchers	Terryn Allen Alfonso LaRon Davis Darin Goines, Sr. Joseph Goines, Jr. Mitchell Goines, Sr. Richard Goines, Sr. T-Bone Goines Albert Lateef
Project Engineer	Vaneitta Goines

Made in the USA
Monee, IL
06 September 2019